The Sailor's Creed

I am a United States sailor.

I will support and defend the Constitution of the United States of America and I will obey the orders of those appointed over me.

I represent the fighting spirit of the Navy and those who have gone before me to defend freedom and democracy around the world.

I proudly serve my country's Navy combat team with honor, courage, and commitment.

I am committed to excellence and the fair treatment of all.

Other books in the **When I Grow Up I Want To Be...**
children's book series by Wigu Publishing:

When I Grow Up I Want To Be...in the U.S. Army!
When I Grow Up I Want To Be...a Teacher!
When I Grow Up I Want To Be...a Firefighter!

Look for these titles in the **When I Grow Up I Want To Be...**
children's book series soon:

When I Grow Up I Want To Be...a Veterinarian!
When I Grow Up I Want To Be...a Nurse!
When I Grow Up I Want To Be...a Good Person!
When I Grow Up I Want To Be...a Race Car Driver!
When I Grow Up I Want To Be...in the U.S. Air Force!
When I Grow Up I Want To Be...a World Traveler!
When I Grow Up I Want To Be...a Police Officer!
When I Grow Up I Want To Be... Green!

Visit www.whenigrowupbooks.com for more information.
Like us at www.facebook.com/whenigrowupbooksbywigu.

When I Grow Up I Want To Be...®

in the U.S. Navy!

NOAH TOURS AN AIRCRAFT CARRIER!

Wigu Publishing | Laguna Beach, CA

Library of Congress Control Number: 2014901052
ISBN 978-1-939973-02-3

Wigu Publishing is a collaboration among talented and creative individuals working together to publish informative and fun books for our children. Our titles serve to introduce children to the people in their communities who serve others through their vocations. Wigu's books are unique in that they help our children to visualize the abundant opportunities that exist for them to be successful and to make a difference. Our goal is to inspire the great leaders and thinkers of tomorrow.

First edition, paperback, 2014
10 9 8 7 6 5 4 3 2 1

Quantity sales: Special discounts are available on quantity purchases by corporations, associations, promotional organizations, and others. For details, please contact the publisher at

Wigu Publishing
Barron Ressler, Publisher
1278 Glenneyre Street
Laguna Beach, CA 92651
inquiries@wigupublishing.com

Visit our website at www.whenigrowupbooks.com for more information.

Proudly printed and bound in the United States of America.

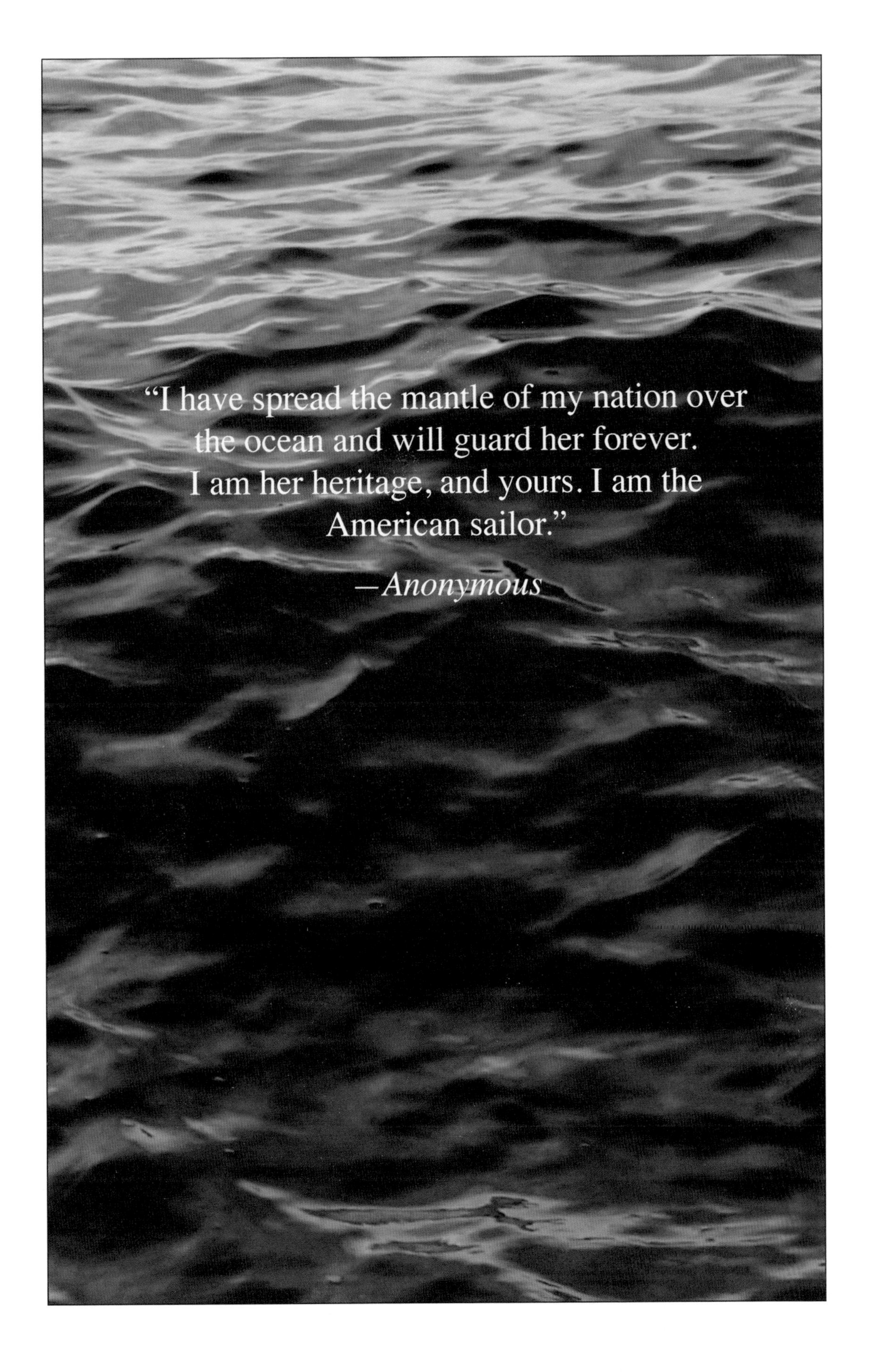
"I have spread the mantle of my nation over
the ocean and will guard her forever.
I am her heritage, and yours. I am the
American sailor."
–*Anonymous*

This is the story of Noah—and his little sister, too! Noah wants to be in the Navy just like his Grandpa Ed. Today is their chance to learn what being in the Navy is all about!

Noah was excited. A U.S. Navy aircraft carrier had come into port. Everyone was invited to visit. Noah's Grandpa Ed promised to take him!

Noah loved to hear all of Grandpa Ed's stories about the years he spent in the Navy, especially the stories about aircraft carriers and fighter planes.

Grandma Marilyn said some of the stories were even true!

The United States Navy is the largest navy in the world, with a proud tradition of serving our country. This legacy goes back to the American Revolution. In 1775, General George Washington ordered the first American ships to fight for our freedom and independence from Great Britain. These first ships were called the Continental Navy.

The first U.S. Navy jack (flag)

USS *Constitution*

After the War of Independence, our new nation needed a larger, stronger military, including the Navy. The Naval Act of 1794 called for six ships to be built. One of those ships, the USS *Constitution*, is now the oldest commissioned Navy ship still afloat. The USS *Constitution* earned the nickname "Old Ironsides" during the War of 1812 because enemy shot, or cannon balls, bounced off its sides.

"When I grow up, I'm going to be in the Navy just like Grandpa Ed," Noah told his little sister, Marina. "He is taking me on a real aircraft carrier today."

"I'm coming, too," said Marina. "I want to be in the Navy, too. I want to go on an aircraft carrier!"

"Does she always have to come along?" asked Noah.

"She's welcome to come!" said Grandpa Ed. "There are lots of women serving in the U.S. Navy, you know."

Marina grinned. Then she asked, "What's an aircraft carrier anyway?"

An aircraft carrier is a sea-going mobile air base, like an airport on the water. The earliest aircraft carriers did not actually carry airplanes. They carried observation balloons.

Today, the United States Navy has a fleet of giant carriers ready for action, with more on the way.

Thanks to these carriers, our country is able to send Navy air power almost anywhere in the world to defend our freedoms and help our friends.

Noah and Marina drove with Grandpa Ed to the Navy pier where the aircraft carrier had docked just the day before.

"Wow, that carrier is huge!" Noah exclaimed as they pulled up.

"Huge," said his sister.

Noah groaned. "She copies everything I say!"

"She copies everything I say!" Marina laughed.

Noah thought better of saying anything more.

"I've told you stories all about when I was in the Navy," said Grandpa Ed. "Today, we are going to learn some new things, and maybe a little patience, too."

"I can't wait," said Noah.

Grandpa smiled.

"An aircraft carrier is filled with sailors doing all kinds of jobs, all with one important purpose," said Grandpa Ed. "Every sailor takes an oath, a promise, to keep this country safe, just like I did when I was in the Navy."

Noah wondered if Grandpa Ed was about to tell one of his Navy stories again.

But he didn't.

Aircraft carriers are the largest warships in the world.

They can be as tall as a 24-story building and as long as three soccer fields placed end to end.

An aircraft carrier can have 18 decks and more than 4,000 different rooms, with over 3,000 televisions and 2,500 telephones.

The crew of an aircraft carrier can number over 5,000 men and women. The pilots and crew that maintain the aircraft are called the Air Wing. The crew that keeps the carrier running is called the Ship's Company.

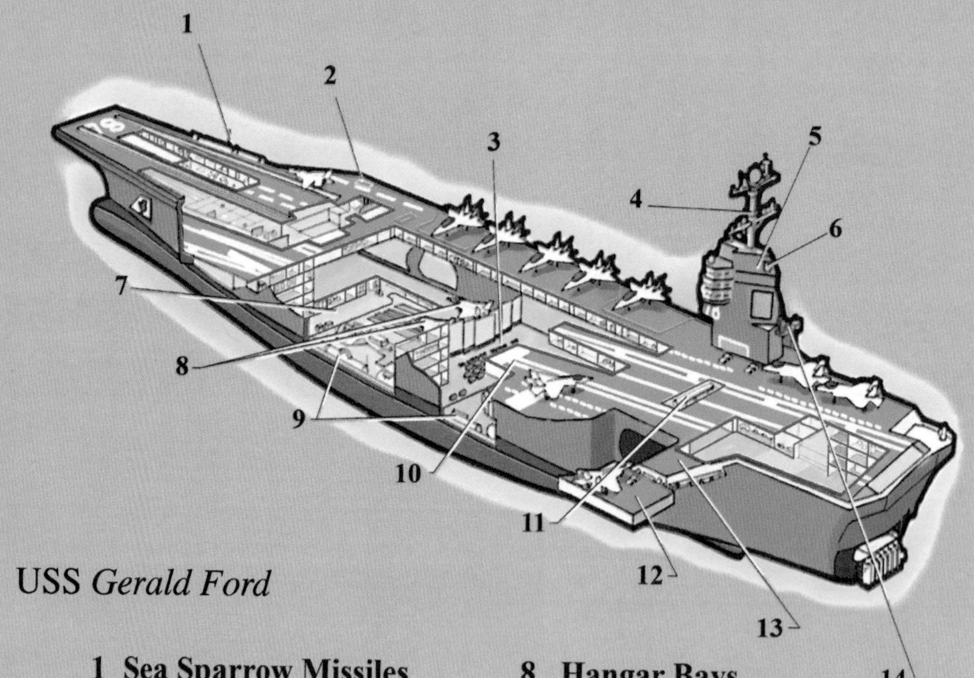

USS *Gerald Ford*

1 Sea Sparrow Missiles
2 Weapon's Elevator
3 Storerooms
4 Mast
5 Island
6 Radar
7 Electrical Room
8 Hangar Bays
9 Nuclear Power Plants
10 Catapults
11 Arresting Gear
12 Aircraft Elevators
13 Flight Deck
14 Landing System

Being in the U.S. Navy requires dedication and sacrifice. It means sailors can often be away from home, family, and friends for months or even years... often in harm's way.

“Look at that huge anchor!” exclaimed Noah.

“Huge,” said Marina.

“Huge is right!” said Grandpa Ed. “The carrier needs two huge anchors, one on each side. There’s a special crew just to handle them.”

Noah asked, “If everyone on the ship is supposed to keep us safe, how does the anchor crew do that?”

“They drop the anchor on bad guys!” said Marina.

“Not quite,” said Grandpa Ed. “When the ship needs to stop, the crew drops the anchor so the carrier won’t drift away or bump into another ship. Keeping the ship safe keeps us safe. No ship is safe without one.”

Today's aircraft-carrier anchor can weigh more than 30 tons, the weight of about 15 adult bull elephants. The anchor is so important that it has long been a symbol adopted by the U.S. Navy and by navies around the world.

"Let's be careful walking up the gangplank," said Grandpa Ed. "Hold your sister's hand, Noah."

"The gangplank?" Noah smiled. "Did pirates really make people walk the plank?"

"I think so," said Grandpa Ed.

“Are there still pirates, Grandpa Ed?” asked Marina.

“Yes, but not like in the movies.”

“Were girls pirates, too?” asked Marina.

“Yep. They sure were,” said Grandpa Ed.

Blackbeard the Pirate

Noah nudged his sister. “Maybe we’ll make you walk the plank!”

She stuck her tongue out at him.

Grandpa Ed smiled. “The U.S. Navy doesn’t make anyone walk the plank. If you don’t behave, the Navy can put you in the ship’s jail, called the Brig.”

“Were you ever in the Brig, Grandpa Ed?” asked Noah.

“Were you?” repeated Marina.

Grandpa Ed laughed. “Why don’t we just go see what’s up ahead?”

Our country has built a strong navy to protect us from pirates and other bad guys wherever they may be. Every sailor in the U.S. Navy plays an important part in this mission.

The backbone of the U.S. Navy is the aircraft carrier. The carrier is often combined with support ships to make up a Carrier Strike Group.

An aircraft carrier functions like a city, with its own post office (with its own ZIP code), bank, gym, and hospital. To take care of the ship and its sailors, there are doctors, dentists, barbers, electricians, plumbers, cooks, carpenters, mechanics, and firefighters.

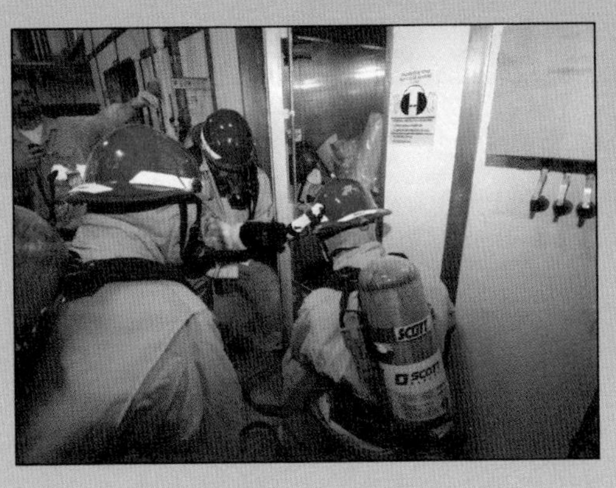

"Look over here. The deckhands are swabbing the deck."

"What's 'swabbing the deck' mean?" asked Noah.

"Swabbing means mopping," said Grandpa Ed. "The deckhands make sure the runways are clean and clear so the aircraft can take off and land safely. The crew keeps the whole ship clean and free of clutter so everyone can get to their jobs to keep us safe."

"Yeah, Mom is always after me to pick up my stuff," said Noah.

Marina rolled her eyes and said, "I wonder why!"

"Let's go visit the sailors' quarters," said Grandpa Ed. "The ship's crew sleeps in bunk beds."

"I want to be on a top bunk," said Noah.

"I want to be on a top bunk, too," said Marina.

"If you're the captain, you get your own private cabin like this one here," Grandpa Ed told them.

Marina's eyes brightened. "Really?"

"Where did you sleep?" asked Noah.

"I slept in a bunk bed, but it wasn't anywhere near this nice," said Grandpa Ed. "Right between two guys who snored."

"Grandma Marilyn says you snore," said Marina.

"Grandma Marilyn should talk!" Grandpa Ed chuckled. "Anyway, let's just see the rest of the ship, ok?"

Grandpa Ed led Noah and Marina to a narrow flight of stairs.

“These steps are a really tight fit. The halls are skinnier than at my school,” said Noah.

Grandpa Ed nodded. “I bumped my head and banged my knees plenty of times and I was a bit slimmer then. I could move a lot faster, too!”

"I smell something cooking," said Noah.

"Smells good," said Marina.

"This is the mess deck. It's like your school cafeteria but much bigger. The cooks prepare meals in the galley," said Grandpa Ed. "The Navy calls the cooks 'culinary specialists.' It's a pretty special job to cook for 5,000 hungry sailors three times a day, plus snacks."

"How can the cooks keep us safe?" asked Noah. "Do they throw french fries at bad guys like a food fight?"

"I like french fries," said Marina. "Do they have french fries with ketchup?"

"I think they have just about anything you'd want," said Grandpa Ed. "The cooks make sure all the sailors on board get healthy meals so they can do their jobs, which keeps us safe. It takes a lot of hard work, and there are a lot of pots and pans and dishes to wash afterward, too."

"Now I want you to see what powers this ship," said Grandpa Ed.

"Who are those guys?" asked Noah.

"Yeah, who are those guys?" repeated Marina.

"That's the engine crew. These sailors make sure the ship's power plant provides electricity to light the lights and power the equipment. There's a special crew to run the nuclear reactors that turn the propellers to make the ship go where it's needed."

At first, wind and sail powered our Navy's big ships. The smaller boats, like the lifeboats, could be rowed.

Wind power is free but unreliable. Without wind the ship could not sail.

In 1812, an American engineer and inventor named Robert Fulton built the first Navy steamship. From that point on, each new generation of steam-driven naval warships became more and more fearsome and powerful.

Battle of the *Monitor* and the *Merrimack*

Today, nuclear energy drives the largest, newest Navy ships, the most powerful ships in the history of the world.

"What's behind that door?" asked Noah.

"That's where the crew runs the nuclear reactors," said Grandpa Ed.

"How do they keep us safe?" asked Noah.

"By not letting us in there," said Grandpa Ed.

"Couldn't we just take a peek?" Marina asked.

"What does the sign say?" Grandpa Ed replied.

The nuclear reactors that propel the Navy's newest aircraft carriers are more powerful than 500 race cars combined. The energy provided by these reactors can run a ship for more than 20 years without refueling.

The energy is created from radioactive material, called uranium, and can be dangerous if not properly controlled. Nuclear-powered ships are designed to be as safe as possible, so they do not create air or water pollution as they travel the seas of the world.

"Now let's go to the hangar deck. The hangar deck is where the aircraft are stored and where the mechanics work to keep them in good shape," Grandpa Ed said.

"The mechanics keep us safe by taking care of the ship and the airplanes," said Noah.

"Right," said Grandpa Ed. "The mechanics are busy at work throughout the carrier. There are millions of parts on the ship which must be kept in perfect working order. If someone breaks anything, the mechanics know how to fix it."

"Did you ever break anything when you were in the Navy?" asked Noah.

"Why don't we just see what's up ahead?" said Grandpa Ed.

"Is the hangar deck where they put rockets and bombs on the planes?" asked Noah.

"As I remember that is usually done up on the flight deck. The planes are lifted to the flight deck by those giant elevators. Then the ordnance crews load the weapons."

"Now you're talking!" said Noah. "Bombs away!"

"Well, not right away," said Grandpa Ed.

The hangar deck is located beneath the flight deck.

Up to 100 aircraft can be stored there. The mechanics keep the aircraft ready for action.

When it's time to fly, the aircraft are lifted up to the flight deck on giant elevators, each powerful and big enough to lift two 74,000-pound fighter jets at the same time.

“This is the flight deck,” said Grandpa Ed. “Normally they don’t let a lot of people up here. It’s dangerous when aircraft are flying in and out. You can see why it is so important for the crew to keep it clean and clear.”

“The flight deck is really cool,” said Noah.

“It can also be dangerous!” said Grandpa Ed. “Those planes are taking off and landing night and day, armed with bombs and rockets.

“If they are not careful, crewmembers can be blown overboard into the sea or sucked into a plane’s engine. Everyone has to be in the right place at the right time.”

The flight deck looks like an airport runway, but it's much shorter, so airplanes need an extra boost to take off safely.

The first boost comes as the carrier is turned into the wind, which creates more airflow to help lift the plane like wind lifts a kite.

The second boost comes from the plane's powerful jet engines.

The next boost comes from catapults, like giant slingshots, that shoot the plane down the runway.

Giant blast deflectors rise up behind the plane, protecting the crew and planes nearby from the heat of the engines.

The pilot is cleared to take off. The engines are ignited.

The catapult is released, speeding the plane down the runway from 0 to 170 miles per hour in two seconds.

As the plane clears the carrier deck, the jet engines roar to maximum power, thrusting the plane faster than the speed of sound.

"I know how pilots keep us safe, too," said Noah. "Pilots fly and fight bad guys!"

"Yeah!" Marina stretched out her arms and pretended to fly around Noah again and again, as if he were the bad guy. He held up his hands to stop her.

"You can stop now, Marina," said Noah.

"Sometimes you don't have to fight. Sometimes just having a powerful Navy is enough to keep the bad guys in line," said Grandpa Ed. "But there are times when the people who protect us have to go into harm's way."

"Well, it must be cool to be a pilot in the Navy!"

"Being a Navy pilot is cool," said Grandpa Ed. "But it's not easy. Even take off and landing are hard—especially when the sea is tossing and turning the ship every which way. It takes a lot of training and skill to be a Navy pilot."

"See? You have to go to school to be a pilot," Noah said to Marina. "It takes a lot more than just running around in circles!"

Marina kept buzzing around.

It takes more than two years of intense training to be a Navy pilot.

Trainees begin at Ground School. They study many drills and rules. They learn what all the instruments on the plane's control panel are for.

Later, trainees practice in a flight simulator, which is like an oversized video game.

Finally, when they are skilled enough, the future pilots get to practice in real planes.

"How does the pilot know how to land? It must be really hard. If they go too far they might fall into the ocean," said Noah.

"When I was in the Navy, we waved signal flags to direct the pilot to a safe landing," Grandpa Ed explained. "Now they use flashing lights."

"Like a traffic light?" asked Noah.

"Yes, but with a lot more lights. It isn't just stop and go," said Grandpa Ed.

"Red means stop, green means go," chirped Marina.

"Can someone give Marina a red light?"

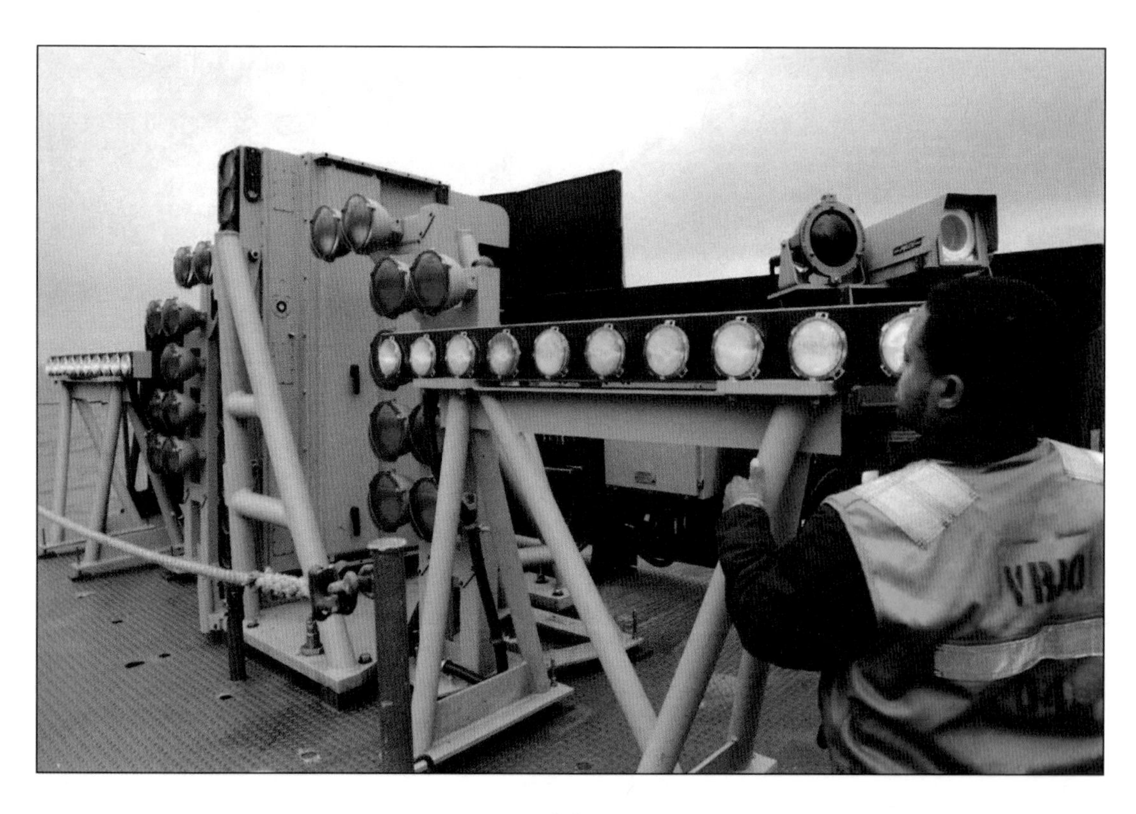

The carrier flight deck has only about 500 feet of runway—it's too short for the heavy, fast-moving airplanes to land on their own. So each plane has a tailhook that comes down as the plane begins its landing approach.

The pilot must land on the deck just right so the tailhook catches onto a heavy steel arresting wire. The wire stretches across the deck and stops the plane in seconds. There are four wires in a row to give pilots four chances.

If the tailhook misses all of the wires, then safety nets can catch the plane before it slides off the deck and into the ocean below.

“Hey, what is that tower?” asked Marina, pointing.

“That tower on top of the ship is called the Island,” said Grandpa Ed. “That’s where the captain runs the ship.”

The Island is the carrier's control center, like the control tower at an airport. The Island is where the captain gives commands to the sailors who sail the ship and to the pilots who fly the aircraft.

At the top of the Island are the antennas that track all sea and air traffic. The captain and crew watch to make sure the ship is on course. They watch for dangers to navigation like hidden reefs, and they watch for enemy planes and ships.

All the sailors depend on each other to keep the carrier running smoothly—just like our country depends on the Navy to keep us safe and sound.

"When I grow up I'm going to be in the Navy for sure," said Noah, "but I am not sure what I am going to do. There are so many jobs!"

“Well, you can always wash the dishes,” said Marina.

Noah scowled.

“Anyway, I know for sure what I’m going to be!” Marina announced. “Try to guess.”

"Who knows?" said Noah. "I'm deciding what I want to be."

"You don't have to decide right now," assured Grandpa Ed.

"You can wash dishes," Marina said again.

"Not funny," answered Noah.

Grandpa Ed chuckled.

“I’ve got it!” said Noah. “I’m going to be a pilot in the U.S. Navy! I’ll have my own helmet and airplane. Whenever anyone is in danger, they will call for me.”

He looked over at Marina and grinned. "So there!"

"So what?" answered Marina.

"So it sounds good!" said Grandpa Ed.

"Well, guess what!" said Marina. "I'm going to have my very own cabin all to myself."

Noah frowned. "That can't be. The only person on the ship who gets a cabin all to himself is…"

"You got it!" said Marina. "You mean 'herself,' don't you?"

"No way," said Noah.

Grandpa Ed smiled.

"You may call me Captain Marina from now on."

Noah thought of a lot of things he could call his little sister besides captain, but he thought better of it.

Well, at least she's not being a copycat, he thought.

Noah smiled. “Ok, Marina. I’ll fly the planes and you can steer the ship. That works. Every job is important, right, Grandpa Ed?”

Grandpa Ed chuckled. “That’s right! And when you both grow up, you’ll have lots of Navy stories to tell your grandkids.”

Marina grinned. “And some of them might even be true!”

CARRIER STRIKE GROUP (CSG)

To help aircraft carriers defend our freedoms, the U.S. Navy assigns an armada of ships to accompany each of the aircraft carriers. Together, they are called Carrier Strike Groups. The carriers and their Air Wings represent the main offensive power while the other ships provide defense and support.

These Carrier Strike Groups are a powerful force for good, working in confined waters and open seas, day and night, in all weather.

These strike groups not only accomplish military missions for our country, they also serve to offer protection and humanitarian aid for our friends and allied nations across the globe.

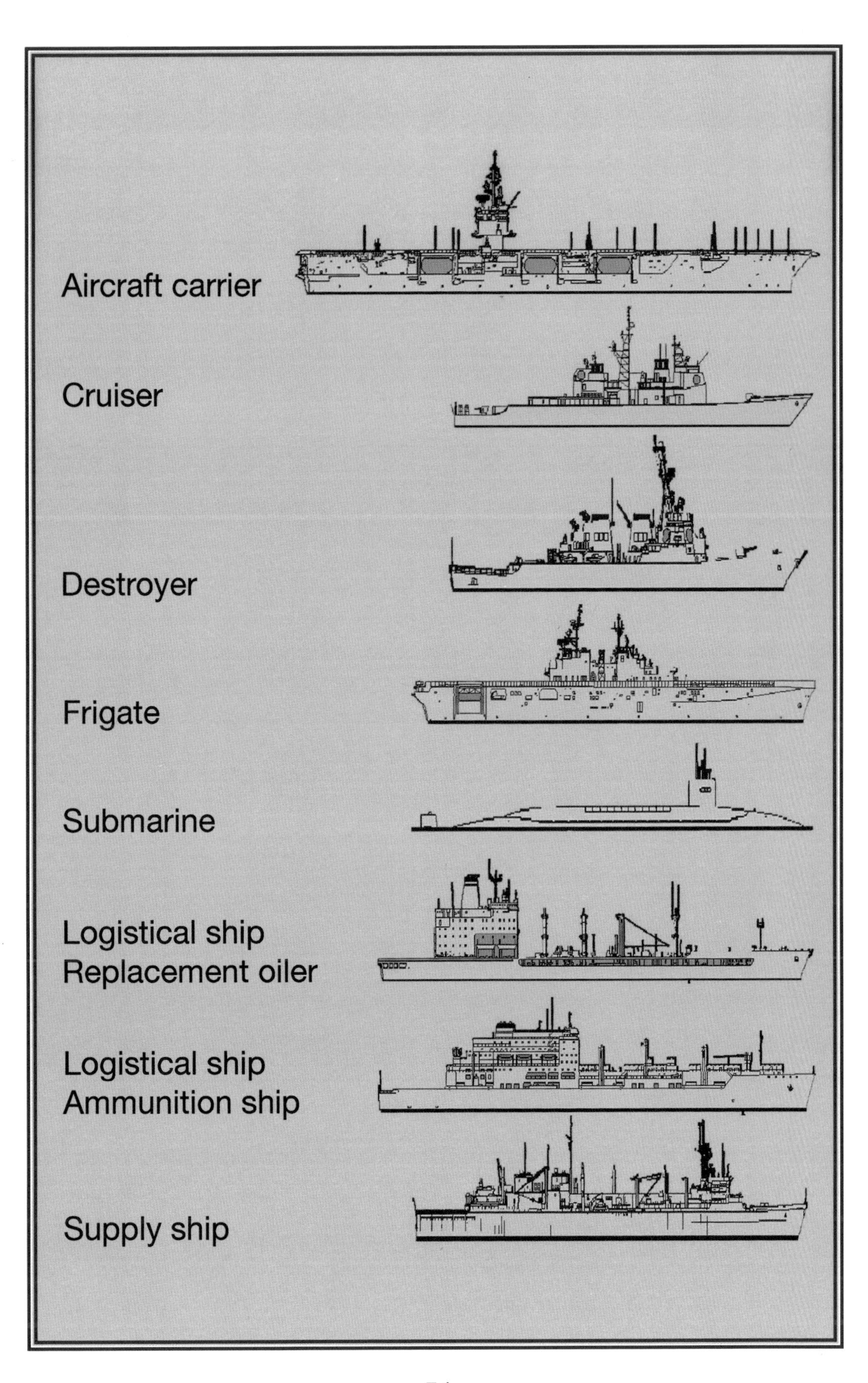
Aircraft carrier
Cruiser
Destroyer
Frigate
Submarine
Logistical ship
Replacement oiler
Logistical ship
Ammunition ship
Supply ship

Image credits

Photos, unless otherwise noted, courtesy of the United States Department of the Navy.

p. 2. Painting: *George Washington,* by Stuart Gilbert. (Source: Wikimedia.)
First navy jack of the United States. (Source: Wikipedia.)

p. 8. USS *Gerald Ford* (CVN-78), courtesy of *Machine Design* magazine.

p. 13. Painting: *Capture of the Pirate, Blackbeard,* 1718, by Jean Leon Gerome Ferris, 1920, courtesy of Creative Commons.

p. 23. Chromolithograph: *The Battle of Hampton Roads,* produced by Louis Prang & Co., Boston, Massachusetts, courtesy of the Library of Congress.

p. 38. Photo: Optical Landing System, courtesy of Creative Commons.

Made in the USA
San Bernardino, CA
25 April 2014